Teacher's Resource Book

D1404900

Mc Graw Hill **Macmillan McGraw-Hill**

Photography Credits

162: S Wanke/PhotoLink. 166: Creatas/PunchStock.

167: John A Rizzo/Getty Images.

B

The **McGraw·Hill** Companies

**Macmillan
McGraw-Hill**

Published by Macmillan/McGraw-Hill, of McGraw-Hill Education, a division of The McGraw-Hill Companies, Inc., Two Penn Plaza, New York, New York 10121.

Printed in the United States of America

3 4 5 6 7 8 9 10 079 11 10 09 08 07 06

Contents

Weekly Student Contracts

Helping Students Manage Their Time

Weekly Student Contracts help students manage their independent work time.

A Student Contract is supplied for each week of instruction in Treasures. The contract lists independent activities provided in the program that support priority skills for the week. The activities listed include:

- workstation activities
- leveled readers and activities
- technology activities
- practice book activities

How to Use the Student Contract

- At the beginning of each week, distribute a contract to each student.

- Discuss with students each activity listed in the contract.

- Identify activities and practice book pages that you expect students to complete by the end of the week.

- As students complete each assigned activity, ask them to check off the completed task on the contract and store their work in a folder.

- Students can choose other activities from the contract after completing the assigned activities.

- Check the work in the folder at the end of each week. The folder can also be sent home for review.

Contracts

My To-Do List

✔ Put a check next to the activities you complete.

📖 Reading

☐ Practice fluency
☐ Read about school contests

Ⓐ🅑🅒 Word Study

☐ Write with synonyms
☐ Use short vowels and variants

✏️ Writing

☐ Write a personal narrative
☐ Write a diary or journal entry

🔍 Science

☐ Research and write about contests
☐ Create a scientific contest

🌎 Social Studies

☐ Research and write about world record holders
☐ Read and discuss your article

📖 Leveled Readers

☐ Write About It!
☐ Content Connection

🖱️ Technology

☐ Vocabulary Puzzlemaker
☐ Fluency Solutions
☐ Listening Library
☐ www.macmillanmh.com

✍️ Independent Practice

☐ Practice Book, I–7
☐ Grammar Practice Book, I–6
☐ Spelling Practice Book, I–6

Name _____ Date _____

My To-Do List

✔ Put a check next to the activities you complete.

 Reading

☐ Practice fluency
☐ Read about a legendary figure

 Word Study

☐ Write and use long-vowel words
☐ Write and use compound words

 Writing

☐ Write a short narrative
☐ Write about yourself

 Science

☐ Research the Old West
☐ Compare it with today

 Social Studies

☐ Research a legendary figure
☐ Create a map of his or her life

 Leveled Readers

☐ Write About It!
☐ Content Connection

 Technology

☐ Vocabulary Puzzlemaker
☐ Fluency Solutions
☐ Listening Library
☐ www.macmillanmh.com

 Independent Practice

☐ Practice Book, 8–14
☐ Grammar Practice Book, 7–12
☐ Spelling Practice Book, 7–12

My To-Do List

✔ Put a check next to the activities you complete.

📖 Reading

- [ ] Practice fluency
- [ ] Read a book about trees

Ⓐ🅑 Word Study

- [ ] Write and use homographs
- [ ] Create a /ü/, /ū/, /u̇/ word chart

✏️ Writing

- [ ] Write a description of a tree
- [ ] Write a descriptive essay

🔍 Science

- [ ] Research types of trees
- [ ] Compare and contrast trees

🌎 Social Studies

- [ ] Research and write about state symbols
- [ ] Draw a picture

Leveled Readers

- [ ] Write About It!
- [ ] Content Connection

🖱 Technology

- [ ] Vocabulary Puzzlemaker
- [ ] Fluency Solutions
- [ ] Listening Library
- [ ] www.macmillanmh.com

Independent Practice

- [ ] Practice Book, 15–21
- [ ] Grammar Practice Book, 13–18
- [ ] Spelling Practice Book, 13–18

Name _____ Date _____

My To-Do List

✔ Put a check next to the activities you complete.

 Reading

- ☐ Practice fluency
- ☐ Read a book about space

 Word Study

- ☐ Write with /är/, /âr/, /ôr/ words
- ☐ Create a context-clues word puzzle

 Writing

- ☐ Write a narrative text
- ☐ Write an informational text

 Science

- ☐ Research Earth and Mars
- ☐ Draw a Venn diagram of differences and similarities

 Social Studies

- ☐ Research astronaut qualities
- ☐ Write a job description

 Leveled Readers

- ☐ Write About It!
- ☐ Content Connection

 Technology

- ☐ Vocabulary Puzzlemaker
- ☐ Fluency Solutions
- ☐ Listening Library
- ☐ www.macmillanmh.com

 Independent Practice

- ☐ Practice Book, 22–28
- ☐ Grammar Practice Book, 19–24
- ☐ Spelling Practice Book, 19–24

My To-Do List

✔ Put a check next to the activities you complete.

Reading

- ☐ Practice fluency
- ☐ Choose a book about dogs

Word Study

- ☐ Look up and listen for /ûr/ and /îr/ words
- ☐ Use a thesaurus for synonyms

Writing

- ☐ Write a journal entry
- ☐ Write an award citation

Science

- ☐ Research dog survival traits
- ☐ Research a suitable pet

Social Studies

- ☐ Research and compare two dog breeds
- ☐ Write a summary

Leveled Readers

- ☐ Write About It!
- ☐ Content Connection

Technology

- ☐ Vocabulary Puzzlemaker
- ☐ Fluency Solutions
- ☐ Listening Library
- ☐ www.macmillanmh.com

Independent Practice

- ☐ Practice Book, 29–35
- ☐ Grammar Practice Book, 25–30
- ☐ Spelling Practice Book, 25–30

My To-Do List

✔ Put a check next to the activities you complete.

 Reading

☐ Practice reading aloud
☐ Read about veterinarians

 Word Study

☐ Work with compound words
☐ Write with idioms

 Writing

☐ Write a public service announcement
☐ Write a letter to a vet

 Science

☐ Research veterinarians
☐ Make a Venn diagram

 Social Studies

☐ Plan a park or square
☐ Illustrate your plan

 Leveled Readers

☐ Write About It!
☐ Content Connection

 Technology

☐ Vocabulary Puzzlemaker
☐ Fluency Solutions
☐ Listening Library
☐ www.macmillanmh.com

Independent Practice

☐ Practice Book, 38–44
☐ Grammar Practice Book, 33–38
☐ Spelling Practice Book, 33–38

My To-Do List

✔ Put a check next to the activities you complete.

📖 Reading

- ☐ Practice fluency
- ☐ Choose a book about snakes

Ⓐ Ⓑ Word Study

- ☐ Work with plurals
- ☐ Write with context clues

✏️ Writing

- ☐ Write a letter to the editor
- ☐ Write a research report

🔍 Science

- ☐ Research snake myths
- ☐ Create a snake myth based on a scientific fact

🌎 Social Studies

- ☐ Research true snake stories
- ☐ Write a letter

📖 Leveled Readers

- ☐ Write About It!
- ☐ Content Connection

🖱️ Technology

- ☐ Vocabulary Puzzlemaker
- ☐ Fluency Solutions
- ☐ Listening Library
- ☐ www.macmillanmh.com

🖌️ Independent Practice

- ☐ Practice Book, 45–51
- ☐ Grammar Practice Book, 39–44
- ☐ Spelling Practice Book, 39–44

Name _____ Date _____

My To-Do List

✔ Put a check next to the activities you complete.

 Reading

☐ Practice fluency

☐ Read about national monuments

 Word Study

☐ Practice with inflected endings *-ed* and *-ing*

☐ Write with *-ed* and *-ing*

 Writing

☐ Write a description

☐ Write with a point of view

 Science

☐ Research building materials

☐ Write about protecting monuments

 Social Studies

☐ Research a monument

☐ Write directions to it

 Leveled Readers

☐ Write About It!

☐ Content Connection

 Technology

☐ Vocabulary Puzzlemaker

☐ Fluency Solutions

☐ Listening Library

☐ www.macmillanmh.com

 Independent Practice

☐ Practice Book, 52–58

☐ Grammar Practice Book, 45–50

☐ Spelling Practice Book, 45–50

My To-Do List

✔ Put a check next to the activities you complete.

📖 Reading

☐ Practice fluency

☐ Choose a cookbook to read

ⒶⒷⒸ Word Study

☐ Analyze words with /o/, /ou/, and /oi/

☐ Work with suffixes

✏️ Writing

☐ Write a persuasive letter

☐ Write a travel article

🔍 Science

☐ Research two countries

☐ Create a Venn diagram

🌎 Social Studies

☐ Research and compare two different islands

☐ Plan a trip

📖 Leveled Readers

☐ Write About It!

☐ Content Connection

🖱️ Technology

☐ Vocabulary Puzzlemaker

☐ Fluency Solutions

☐ Listening Library

☐ www.macmillanmh.com

🖌️ Independent Practice

☐ Practice Book, 59–65

☐ Grammar Practice Book, 51–56

☐ Spelling Practice Book, 51–56

My To-Do List

✔ Put a check next to the activities you complete.

📖 Reading

☐ Practice fluency

☐ Choose a poem to read

(ABC) Word Study

☐ Write words with the VCCV pattern

☐ Work with antonyms

✏ Writing

☐ Write a movie outline

☐ Write a persuasive essay

🔍 Science

☐ Research the American West

☐ Play an Old West quiz

🌎 Social Studies

☐ Research native American tribes

☐ Research lacrosse

📖 Leveled Readers

☐ Write About It!

☐ Content Connection

🖱 Technology

☐ Vocabulary Puzzlemaker

☐ Fluency Solutions

☐ Listening Library

☐ www.macmillanmh.com

🖌 Independent Practice

☐ Practice Book, 66–72

☐ Grammar Practice Book, 57–62

☐ Spelling Practice Book, 57–62

My To-Do List

✔ **Put a check next to the activities you complete.**

 ### Reading

☐ Practice fluency

☐ Read about the Revolution

 ### Word Study

☐ Pronounce V/CV and VC/V patterns

☐ Build word families

 ### Writing

☐ Write a fictional narrative

☐ Write a soldier's letter home

 ### Science

☐ Research Revolutionary artifacts

☐ Draw artifacts

Social Studies

☐ Write a colonist's protest letter

☐ Write King George's response

 ### Leveled Readers

☐ Write About It!

☐ Content Connection

 ### Technology

☐ Vocabulary Puzzlemaker

☐ Fluency Solutions

☐ Listening Library

☐ www.macmillanmh.com

 ### Independent Practice

☐ Practice Book, 75–81

☐ Grammar Practice Book, 65–70

☐ Spelling Practice Book, 65–70

My To-Do List

✔ Put a check next to the activities you complete.

📖 Reading

☐ Practice fluency

☐ Choose an article to read

Ⓐ Ⓑ Ⓒ Word Study

☐ Use V/V patterns

☐ Use a dictionary's pronunciation key

✏️ Writing

☐ Write a fictional narrative

☐ Write a rhyming poem

🔍 Science

☐ Make a chart of voters

☐ Research accuracy of polls

🌎 Social Studies

☐ Research voting history

☐ Create an awards list

📖 Leveled Readers

☐ Write About It!

☐ Content Connection

🖱️ Technology

☐ Vocabulary Puzzlemaker

☐ Fluency Solutions

☐ Listening Library

☐ www.macmillanmh.com

Independent Practice

☐ Practice Book, 82–88

☐ Grammar Practice Book, 71–76

☐ Spelling Practice Book, 71–76

My To-Do List

✔ Put a check next to the activities you complete.

📖 Reading

- ☐ Practice fluency
- ☐ Choose a book on recycling

🅰🅱🅲 Word Study

- ☐ List VCCCV pattern words
- ☐ Use word parts for absorbed prefixes

✏ Writing

- ☐ Write an action letter
- ☐ Write an inventory

🔍 Science

- ☐ Learn about composting
- ☐ Make a composting poster

🌎 Social Studies

- ☐ Write a speech about conserving water
- ☐ Find recycling connections

📖 Leveled Readers

- ☐ Write About It!
- ☐ Content Connection

🖱 Technology

- ☐ Vocabulary Puzzlemaker
- ☐ Fluency Solutions
- ☐ Listening Library
- ☐ www.macmillanmh.com

🖌 Independent Practice

- ☐ Practice Book, 89–95
- ☐ Grammar Practice Book, 77–82
- ☐ Spelling Practice Book, 77–82

Name _____ Date _____

My To-Do List

✔ Put a check next to the activities you complete.

 Reading

☐ Practice fluency

☐ Find an article on deserts

 Word Study

☐ Practice pronouncing accented syllables

☐ Work with synonyms

 Writing

☐ Write a dialogue

☐ List ways you use water

 Science

☐ Research desert temperatures

☐ Learn about desert life

 Social Studies

☐ Research water usage

☐ Make a water-use chart

 Leveled Readers

☐ Write About It!

☐ Content Connection

 Technology

☐ Vocabulary Puzzlemaker

☐ Fluency Solutions

☐ Listening Library

☐ www.macmillanmh.com

 Independent Practice

☐ Practice Book, 96–102

☐ Grammar Practice Book, 83–88

☐ Spelling Practice Book, 83–88

Name _____   Date _____

My To-Do List

✔ Put a check next to the activities you complete.

 Reading

☐ Practice fluency
☐ Select a science fiction book

 Word Study

☐ Write and pronounce words with final /ər/
☐ Work with synonyms

 Writing

☐ Write a diary entry as a robot
☐ Write letters from outer space

 Science

☐ Predict a music device of the future
☐ Draw a picture of your device

 Social Studies

☐ Research radio waves
☐ List uses of radio waves

 Leveled Readers

☐ Write About It!
☐ Content Connection

 Technology

☐ Vocabulary Puzzlemaker
☐ Fluency Solutions
☐ Listening Library
☐ www.macmillanmh.com

Independent Practice

☐ Practice Book, 103–109
☐ Grammar Practice Book, 89–94
☐ Spelling Practice Book, 89–94

My To-Do List

✔ **Put a check next to the activities you complete.**

 Reading

☐ Practice fluency

☐ Read a newspaper article

 Word Study

☐ Write and pronounce words with final /əl/ and /ən/

☐ Make homophone pairs

 Writing

☐ Write about a civil rights leader

☐ Report on the civil rights movement

 Science

☐ Make a science time line of the 1950s and 1960s

☐ Draw conclusions about this time

 Social Studies

☐ Research social movements

☐ Chart social goals

 Leveled Readers

☐ Write About It!

☐ Content Connection

Technology

☐ Vocabulary Puzzlemaker

☐ Fluency Solutions

☐ Listening Library

☐ www.macmillanmh.com

 Independent Practice

☐ Practice Book, 112–118

☐ Grammar Practice Book, 97–102

☐ Spelling Practice Book, 97–102

Name _____ Date _____

My To-Do List

✔ **Put a check next to the activities you complete.**

Reading

- ☐ Practice fluency
- ☐ Choose a book about an unfamiliar animal

Word Study

- ☐ Find and pronounce words with the /ou/ or /ow/ sound
- ☐ Write context clues for unfamiliar words

Writing

- ☐ Write about an animal
- ☐ Write about animal defenses

Science

- ☐ Describe animal adaptation
- ☐ Choose "Best Adaptation"

Social Studies

- ☐ Propose climate changes
- ☐ Describe effects of changes

Leveled Readers

- ☐ Write About It!
- ☐ Content Connection

Technology

- ☐ Vocabulary Puzzlemaker
- ☐ Fluency Solutions
- ☐ Listening Library
- ☐ www.macmillanmh.com

Independent Practice

- ☐ Practice Book, 119–125
- ☐ Grammar Practice Book, 103–108
- ☐ Spelling Practice Book, 103–108

Name _____   Date _____

My To-Do List

✔ Put a check next to the activities you complete.

📕 Reading
- ☐ Practice fluency
- ☐ Read about a political party

Ⓐ⒝ⓒ Word Study
- ☐ Use homographs in sentences
- ☐ Work with prefixes and suffixes

✏ Writing
- ☐ Write an essay
- ☐ Write a dialogue

🔍 Science
- ☐ Research polls
- ☐ Poll a group and record results

🌎 Social Studies
- ☐ Report senators' votes
- ☐ Research a congressional representative

📖 Leveled Readers
- ☐ Write About It!
- ☐ Content Connection

🖱 Technology
- ☐ Vocabulary Puzzlemaker
- ☐ Fluency Solutions
- ☐ Listening Library
- ☐ www.macmillanmh.com

📝 Independent Practice
- ☐ Practice Book, 126–132
- ☐ Grammar Practice Book, 109–114
- ☐ Spelling Practice Book, 109–114

My To-Do List

✔ Put a check next to the activities you complete.

📖 Reading

☐ Practice fluency
☐ Read about extreme weather

Ⓐ🅑🅒 Word Study

☐ Pronounce words with /chər/ and /zhər/
☐ Work with multiple-meaning words

✏ Writing

☐ Write a magazine article
☐ Write a pet-survival poem

🔍 Science

☐ Research effects of a natural disaster
☐ Make a time line

🌎 Social Studies

☐ Research protective measures
☐ Make a safety chart

📖 Leveled Readers

☐ Write About It!
☐ Content Connection

🖱 Technology

☐ Vocabulary Puzzlemaker
☐ Fluency Solutions
☐ Listening Library
☐ www.macmillanmh.com

📝 Independent Practice

☐ Practice Book, 133–139
☐ Grammar Practice Book, 115–120
☐ Spelling Practice Book, 115–120

Name _____ Date _____

My To-Do List

✔ Put a check next to the activities you complete.

📖 Reading

- [ ] Practice fluency
- [ ] Read about a trickster

(ABC) Word Study

- [ ] Work with *-ance* and *-ence*
- [ ] Write ten analogies

✏️ Writing

- [ ] Write an interview
- [ ] Create lessons on how to spot a trickster

🔍 Science

- [ ] Explain the role of science in a story
- [ ] Rewrite the story

🌎 Social Studies

- [ ] Describe new fable characters
- [ ] Write a modern fable

📖 Leveled Readers

- [ ] Write About It!
- [ ] Content Connection

🖱️ Technology

- [ ] Vocabulary Puzzlemaker
- [ ] Fluency Solutions
- [ ] Listening Library
- [ ] www.macmillanmh.com

Independent Practice

- [ ] Practice Book, 140–146
- [ ] Grammar Practice Book, 121–126
- [ ] Spelling Practice Book, 121–126

My To-Do List

✔ Put a check next to the activities you complete.

 Reading

☐ Practice fluency
☐ Choose a book to read

 Word Study

☐ Write a story that uses soft *g* words
☐ Use affixes

 Writing

☐ Write a speech
☐ Write a description

 Science

☐ Research animal adaptations
☐ Write a descriptive paragraph

 Social Studies

☐ Research geographical features
☐ Create Venn diagrams

 Leveled Readers

☐ Write About It!
☐ Content Connection

Technology

☐ Vocabulary Puzzlemaker
☐ Fluency Solutions
☐ Listening Library
☐ www.macmillanmh.com

 Independent Practice

☐ Practice Book, 149–155
☐ Grammar Practice Book, 129–134
☐ Spelling Practice Book, 129–134

My To-Do List

✔ Put a check next to the activities you complete.

📖 Reading

- ☐ Practice fluency
- ☐ Choose a book to read

🔤 Word Study

- ☐ Look up pairs of homophones
- ☐ Find the origins of words

✏️ Writing

- ☐ Write a comic dialogue
- ☐ Describe an invention

🔍 Science

- ☐ Research how to grow tomatoes
- ☐ Explain how to grow bigger and better tomatoes

🌎 Social Studies

- ☐ Research food technology
- ☐ Write about some good and bad effects of food technology

📖 Leveled Readers

- ☐ Write About It!
- ☐ Content Connection

🖱️ Technology

- ☐ Vocabulary Puzzlemaker
- ☐ Fluency Solutions
- ☐ Listening Library
- ☐ www.macmillanmh.com

🖌️ Independent Practice

- ☐ Practice Book, 156–162
- ☐ Grammar Practice Book, 135–140
- ☐ Spelling Practice Book, 135–140

Contracts

Name _____ Date _____

My To-Do List

✔ Put a check next to the activities you complete.

📕 Reading

- ☐ Practice fluency
- ☐ Choose a book to read

ⒶⒷⒸ Word Study

- ☐ Form words with prefixes
- ☐ List words and their antonyms

✏️ Writing

- ☐ Write about a nature topic
- ☐ Write about an exploration you'd like to make

🔍 Science

- ☐ Research Lewis and Clark
- ☐ Draw a natural object and write a detailed label

🌎 Social Studies

- ☐ Research nature's impact on society
- ☐ Research society's impact on nature

📖 Leveled Readers

- ☐ Write About It!
- ☐ Content Connection

🖱️ Technology

- ☐ Vocabulary Puzzlemaker
- ☐ Fluency Solutions
- ☐ Listening Library
- ☐ www.macmillanmh.com

✏️ Independent Practice

- ☐ Practice Book, 163–169
- ☐ Grammar Practice Book, 141–146
- ☐ Spelling Practice Book, 141–146

Name _____ Date _____

My To-Do List

✔ Put a check next to the activities you complete.

📕 Reading

- [ ] Practice fluency
- [ ] Choose a book to read

🖊 Writing

- [ ] Write about Samuel Morse
- [ ] Describe how animals communicate

🌎 Social Studies

- [ ] Research how quilts were used as signals in the Civil War
- [ ] Design a coded-message quilt

🖱 Technology

- [ ] Vocabulary Puzzlemaker
- [ ] Fluency Solutions
- [ ] Listening Library
- [ ] www.macmillanmh.com

Ⓐ Word Study

- [ ] Write words with suffixes
- [ ] Make up and define a new word

🔍 Science

- [ ] Research codes in nature
- [ ] List science problems to solve

📖 Leveled Readers

- [ ] Write About It!
- [ ] Content Connection

🖌 Independent Practice

- [ ] Practice Book, 170–176
- [ ] Grammar Practice Book, 147–152
- [ ] Spelling Practice Book, 147–152

Contracts

My To-Do List

✔ **Put a check next to the activities you complete.**

📕 Reading

- ☐ Practice fluency
- ☐ Choose a book to read

Ⓐ🅑Ⓒ Word Study

- ☐ List words with suffix -ion
- ☐ Work with Latin-root words

✏️ Writing

- ☐ Write a descriptive poem
- ☐ Write a point-of-view story

🔍 Science

- ☐ Research parasites and symbiosis
- ☐ Make a symbiosis chart

🌎 Social Studies

- ☐ Research animal migration
- ☐ Draw a migration map

📖 Leveled Readers

- ☐ Write About It!
- ☐ Content Connection

🖱️ Technology

- ☐ Vocabulary Puzzlemaker
- ☐ Fluency Solutions
- ☐ Listening Library
- ☐ www.macmillanmh.com

📝 Independent Practice

- ☐ Practice Book, 177–183
- ☐ Grammar Practice Book, 153–158
- ☐ Spelling Practice Book, 153–158

My To-Do List

✔ Put a check next to the activities you complete.

📚 Reading

☐ Practice fluency

☐ Choose a fairy tale to read

🔤 Word Study

☐ Analyze words with Greek roots

☐ Match homophones

✏️ Writing

☐ Write an eyewitness account

☐ Write a "Be-Careful-What-You-Wish-For" story

🔍 Science

☐ Research an old wives' tale

☐ Discuss any scientific basis for your tale

🌎 Social Studies

☐ Compare two Cinderella tales

☐ Discuss why Cinderella tales are so popular

📖 Leveled Readers

☐ Write About It!

☐ Content Connection

🖱️ Technology

☐ Vocabulary Puzzlemaker

☐ Fluency Solutions

☐ Listening Library

☐ www.macmillanmh.com

✍️ Independent Practice

☐ Practice Book, 186–192

☐ Grammar Practice Book, 161–166

☐ Spelling Practice Book, 161–166

My To-Do List

✔ **Put a check next to the activities you complete.**

📖 Reading

☐ Practice fluency

☐ Choose a book to read

🔤 Word Study

☐ Analyze words with Latin roots

☐ Use multiple-meaning words

✏️ Writing

☐ Write a visitor's guide to a park

☐ Write about preserving a place

🔍 Science

☐ Research how science helps run parks

☐ Write a job-application letter

🌎 Social Studies

☐ Research how parks help communities

☐ Draw a historic-park poster

📖 Leveled Readers

☐ Write About It!

☐ Content Connection

🖱️ Technology

☐ Vocabulary Puzzlemaker

☐ Fluency Solutions

☐ Listening Library

☐ www.macmillanmh.com

🖌️ Independent Practice

☐ Practice Book, 193–199

☐ Grammar Practice Book, 167–172

☐ Spelling Practice Book, 167–172

My To-Do List

✔ Put a check next to the activities you complete.

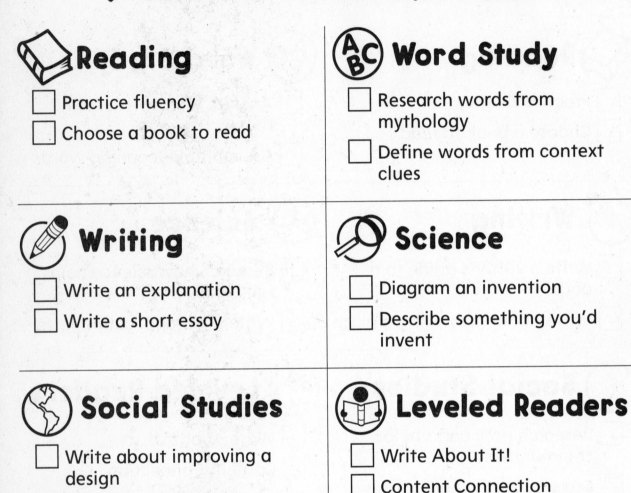

Reading
- ☐ Practice fluency
- ☐ Choose a book to read

Word Study
- ☐ Research words from mythology
- ☐ Define words from context clues

Writing
- ☐ Write an explanation
- ☐ Write a short essay

Science
- ☐ Diagram an invention
- ☐ Describe something you'd invent

Social Studies
- ☐ Write about improving a design
- ☐ Draw your improvement

Leveled Readers
- ☐ Write About It!
- ☐ Content Connection

Technology
- ☐ Vocabulary Puzzlemaker
- ☐ Fluency Solutions
- ☐ Listening Library
- ☐ www.macmillanmh.com

Independent Practice
- ☐ Practice Book, 200–206
- ☐ Grammar Practice Book, 173–178
- ☐ Spelling Practice Book, 173–178

My To-Do List

✔ Put a check next to the activities you complete.

 Reading

☐ Practice fluency

☐ Choose a book to read

 Word Study

☐ Work with number prefixes

☐ Use words with Greek roots

Writing

☐ Write an explanation

☐ Write a vivid description

 Science

☐ Research weather balloons

☐ Make generalizations about weather balloons

 Social Studies

☐ Research how hot-air balloons have changed history

☐ Create a time line

 Leveled Readers

☐ Write About It!

☐ Content Connection

 Technology

☐ Vocabulary Puzzlemaker

☐ Fluency Solutions

☐ Listening Library

☐ www.macmillanmh.com

 Independent Practice

☐ Practice Book, 207–213

☐ Grammar Practice Book, 179–184

☐ Spelling Practice Book, 179–184

Name _____ Date _____

My To-Do List

✔ **Put a check next to the activities you complete.**

Reading
- [ ] Practice fluency
- [ ] Choose a book to read

Word Study
- [ ] Work with suffixes
- [ ] Use words with Latin and Greek word parts

Writing
- [ ] Write an essay
- [ ] Write about a process

Science
- [ ] Research a famous scientist
- [ ] List events in sequence

Social Studies
- [ ] Research a nature myth
- [ ] List ways folk tales can teach science

Leveled Readers
- [ ] Write About It!
- [ ] Content Connection

Technology
- [ ] Vocabulary Puzzlemaker
- [ ] Fluency Solutions
- [ ] Listening Library
- [ ] www.macmillanmh.com

Independent Practice
- [ ] Practice Book, 214–220
- [ ] Grammar Practice Book, 185–190
- [ ] Spelling Practice Book, 185–190

Contracts

Foldables™
by Dinah Zike

What are Foldables™?

Foldables are multi-dimensional graphic organizers that can be used for skills reinforcement, practice, and/or information organizing.

Why use Foldables™?

Not only do Foldables reinforce skills and strategies essential for reading success, they provide a kinesthetic tool for organizing and analyzing learning.

Foldables

Dear Teacher,

A Foldable is a three-dimensional, student-made (and/or teacher-made) interactive graphic organizer based upon a skill. Making a Foldable gives students a fast, kinesthetic activity that helps them organize and retain information either before, during, or after reading. In this section of the *Teacher's Resource Book*, you will find instructions for making Foldables, as well as ideas on how to use them to reinforce and practice phonics, vocabulary, spelling, and comprehension skills.

In this section, you will find Foldables to help you
- replace photocopied activity sheets with student-generated print
- present content and skills in a clear, visual, kinesthetic format
- incorporate the use of such skills as comparing and contrasting, recognizing cause and effect, and finding similarities and differences
- assess student progress and learning levels
- immerse students in new and previously learned vocabulary and reading skills
- teach students unique ways to make study guides and practice materials, and
- provide students with a sense of ownership in their learning.

I am excited to hand these Foldable ideas and activities over to you and your students. Have fun using, adding to, and amending them to meet individual needs.

Sincerely,

Dinah Zike

Creating and Storing Foldables™

As you use the Foldables outlined in this *Teacher's Resource Book*, discuss with students how they can adapt them to make their own Foldable learning and study aids. Teach students to write—titles, vocabulary words, concepts, skills, questions, main ideas—on the front tabs of their Foldables. By doing this, key concepts are viewed every time a student looks at a Foldable. Foldables help students focus on and remember the information presented without being distracted by other print. Remind students to write more specific information—supporting ideas, examples of a concept, definitions, answers to questions, observations—under the tabs.

Turn one-gallon freezer bags into student portfolios and storage containers for Foldables.

Cut the bottom corners off each bag so they won't hold air and will stack and store easily.

Write student names across the top of the plastic portfolios with a permanent marker and cover the writing with two-inch clear tape to keep it from wearing off.

Place a piece of cardboard inside each portfolio to give it strength and to act as a divider.

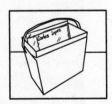

Store Foldables in a giant laundry soap box. Or, students can carry their portfolios in a three-ring binder if you place a strip of two-inch clear tape along one side and punch three holes through the taped edge.

in this section

Basic Shapes
by Dinah Zike

These figures illustrate the basic folds that are referred to throughout the following section of this book.

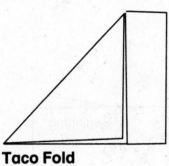

Taco Fold

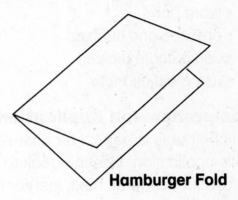

Hamburger Fold

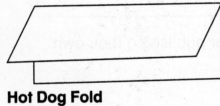

Hot Dog Fold

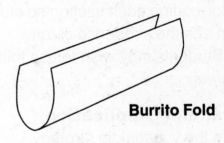

Burrito Fold

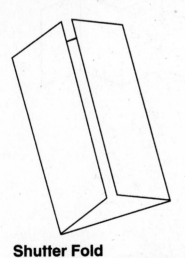

Shutter Fold

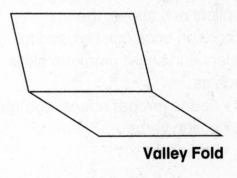

Valley Fold

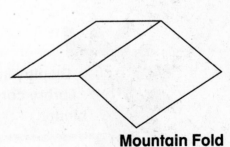

Mountain Fold

Foldables

Using the Accordion Book Foldable™
by Dinah Zike

Vocabulary and Vocabulary Strategy Applications
Use this Foldable to create vocabulary books that record examples and explanations on topics such as:
- word parts
- prefixes and suffixes
- using context clues
- using a dictionary

Comprehension Application
This Foldable is perfect for post-reading skills application. Use the book to record text sequence (first, next, last) or plot sequence (beginning, middle, end). Try color-coding each section so students can see the sequence clearly.

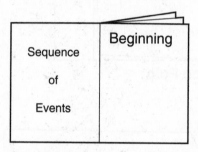

Students may wish to use this Foldable for publishing their own stories.

Grammar Application
Like the vocabulary strategy applications above, the accordion book can be used to collect and share grammar skills such as:

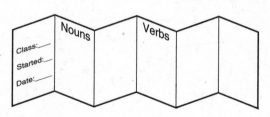

- nouns (proper nouns, common nouns)
- action verbs
- adjectives

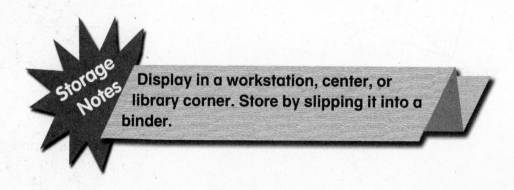

Storage Notes Display in a workstation, center, or library corner. Store by slipping it into a binder.

Accordion Book Foldable™ Directions

by Dinah Zike

Materials:

- several sheets of 11" × 17" paper
- glue

Directions:

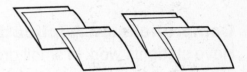

1. Fold each sheet of paper like a hamburger, but fold one side half an inch shorter than the other side. This will form a tab that is half an inch long.

2. Fold this tab forward over the shorter side, then fold it back away from the shorter piece of paper. (In other words, fold it the opposite way.)

3. To form an accordion, glue a straight edge of one section into the valley of another section's tab.

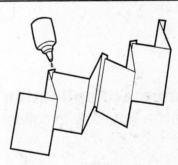

Tips! *Before gluing, stand the sections on end to form an accordion. This will help you see how to glue the sections together. Use different colors of paper to indicate sections of the book. Always place the extra tab at the back of the book so you can add more pages later.*

Foldables

Using the Standing Cube Foldable™
by Dinah Zike

Vocabulary Application
Use the Foldable for developing vocabulary concepts with students. Each side of the cube can show information about a word, such as its definition, example sentences, an illustration, and so on.

Comprehension Application
Have students work in small groups to create a Foldable about a story character they are studying. Each side of the Foldable should illustrate or tell about character traits.

Grammar Application
Use the Foldable to collect and share types of nouns or adjectives.

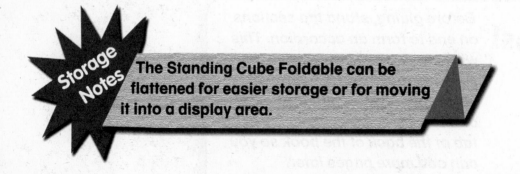

Storage Notes The Standing Cube Foldable can be flattened for easier storage or for moving it into a display area.

Standing Cube Foldable™ Directions
by Dinah Zike

Materials:
- two sheets of 11" × 17" paper
- glue

Directions:

1. Fold each sheet like a hamburger, but fold one side one-half inch shorter than the other side.

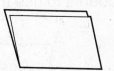

2. Fold the long side over the short side on both sheets of paper, making tabs.

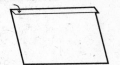

3. On one of the folded papers, place a small amount of glue along the tab, next to the valley but not in it.

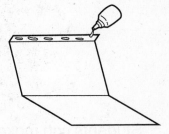

4. Place the non-folded edge of the second sheet of paper square into the valley and fold the glue-covered tab over this sheet of paper. Press flat until the glue holds. Repeat with the other side.

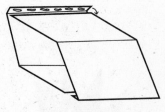

5. Allow the glue to dry completely before continuing. After the glue has dried, collapse the cube flat to write or draw on each side.

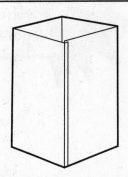

Foldables

Using the Large Word Study Book Foldable™
by Dinah Zike

Vocabulary and Phonics/Spelling Applications

With a small group, make a Foldable for vocabulary word study/review. Display the book in a workstation for repeated review. The size and the format also make it easy for you and students to use them as lap flashcards.

experiment

a test to see how something works

The scientist did an experiment to see what kind of food mice prefer.

Students can make individual books using this Foldable.

Storage Notes Collect and use these books through the year. Store each large book in a labeled legal-size folder.

Large Word Study Book Foldable™ Directions
by Dinah Zike

Materials:
- several sheets of 11" × 17" paper (one sheet for each word studied)
- stapler

Directions:

1. Fold each sheet like a hot dog, but fold one side one inch shorter than the other side.

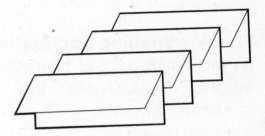

2. Stack the sheets so the folds are side by side.

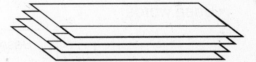

3. Staple sheets together along the tabbed end (the bottom of the pages).

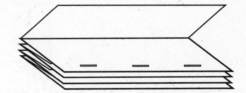

You can make a large word study book as an aid for vocabulary or spelling word lists. On the front of each tab, write a vocabulary or spelling word. Open the tab and write the definition and a sample sentence.

Use this Foldable to _____

_____

_____

_____

Foldables

Using the Layered Book Foldable™
by Dinah Zike

Vocabulary Application
Have students create this Foldable to help them review vocabulary words. Have them write a word on each tab and then flip the tab to write the definition. The same thing can be done with antonyms and synonyms.

Phonics/Spelling Application
A review/study guide of letter sounds and word parts can be done with this Foldable. For example:
- Short vowels
- Long vowels
- Prefixes and suffixes
- Base words

Base Words
strong
fast
high
small

Comprehension Application
Use the Foldable to aid in the following skills reinforcement:
- Character study (one tab per story character)
- Summarize
- Generating Questions

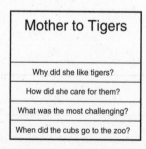

Mother to Tigers
Why did she like tigers?
How did she care for them?
What was the most challenging?
When did the cubs go to the zoo?

Study Skills and Grammar Applications
This Foldable can be used to review/reinforce concepts studied.

Layered Book Foldable™ Directions
by Dinah Zike

Materials:
- two sheets of 8½" × 11" paper
- glue

Directions:

1. Stack two sheets of paper so that the back sheet is one inch higher than the front sheet.

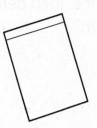

---

2. Bring the bottom of both sheets upward and align the edges so that all of the layers or tabs are the same distance apart.

---

3. When all tabs are an equal distance apart, fold the papers and crease well.

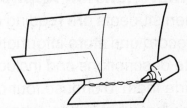

---

4. Open the papers and glue them together along the valley, or inner center fold, or staple them along the mountain.

Tip! *If you need more layers, use additional sheets of paper. Make the tabs smaller than one inch.*

Use this Foldable to _____

Foldables

Using the Four-Door Foldable™
by Dinah Zike

Grammar Application

Use this Foldable for information occurring in four categories. Have students create study guides and review grammar concepts such as four types of sentences. They may label each door with a type of sentence, then define each type and provide an example inside each door.

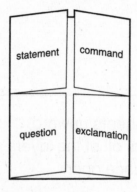

Comprehension Application

When students are reading a selection, they can use this Foldable to record and store information for summarizing. Have students write descriptions and include illustrations inside the four doors. Guide them to choose four categories of information. For example:

- who, what, when, where
- what, where, when, why/how
- character, plot, setting, conflict and resolution

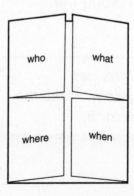

Foldables

Four-Door Foldable™ Directions
by Dinah Zike

Materials:
- sheet of 11" × 17" paper
- scissors

Directions:

1. Make a shutter fold.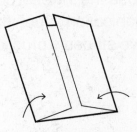

_____

2. Fold the shutter fold in half like a hamburger. Crease well.

_____

3. Open the folds and cut along the inside valley fold lines.

_____

4. These cuts will form four doors on the inside of the book.

Use this Foldable to _____

_____

_____

_____

_____

Using the Two- and Three-Tab Foldable™
by Dinah Zike

Phonics/Spelling Application
Several options adapt this Foldable for prefix, base word, suffix study and practice.

Use the Three-Tab Foldable to help students with word parts and syllabication. Open the tabs and write a base word in the center. Have students practice decoding words.

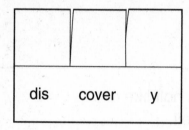

Another option is to cut only one of the valleys (see p. 50) so that the Foldable has two tabs of unequal size. Open the two tabs and write a base word on the bottom paper so that one word part is shown in each box. For further practice with pronunciation and word identification, fold the tabs over to make another word.

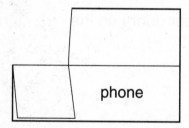

A third option is to make a two-tab variation. Use it to compare two different phonic/spelling elements such as soft *c* and hard *c*, vowel spellings, or word parts.

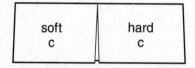

Directions and diagrams appear on page 50.

Using the Two- and Three-Tab Foldables™ *continued*
by Dinah Zike

Comprehension Application

Use large poster board and choose a vertical or horizontal orientation to adapt the Three-Tab Foldable. Use it to create the following graphic organizers:

• Venn Diagram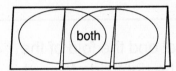

• Story Map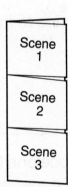

• K-W-L Chart

• Nonfiction text organizer

Directions and diagrams appear on page 50.

© Macmillan/McGraw-Hill

Two- and Three-Tab Foldables™ Directions
by Dinah Zike

Materials:
- one 8½″ × 11″ sheet of paper or large poster board
- scissors

Directions:

1. Fold the sheet like a hot dog.

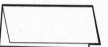

---

2. With the paper horizontal and the fold of the hot dog at the top, fold the right side toward the center, to cover one half of the paper.

---

3. Fold the left side over the right side to make three sections.

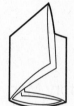

---

4. Open the right and left folds. Place one hand between the two thicknesses of paper and cut up the two valleys so there are three tabs.

Options:
- Cut only one of the valleys so the Foldable has two tabs of unequal size.
- Use large poster board to make a Foldable on which you can record more information.

Use this Foldable to _____

_____

Using the Four- and Eight-Tab Foldable™
by Dinah Zike

Phonics/Spelling Application

Adapt the Four-Tab Foldable to review digraphs, blends, and vowel variant letter-sounds. Open the tabs and write a CVCe word on the bottom paper so that one letter is shown in each box. Have students practice identifying words.

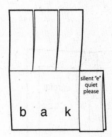

Another option is to make the Foldable with three tabs. At step 3 (see page 53), cut only the first and the third creases so that the middle tab is twice the size of the other two tabs. Open all three tabs and write a CVVC word on the bottom paper so that one letter is shown in each box and so that the middle two letters will be hidden by the middle tab.

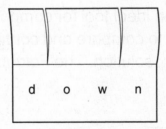

Or, cut only the first and second tabs and write a word that ends with double letters.

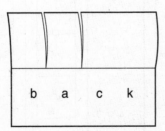

Directions and diagrams appear on page 53.

Foldables

Using the Four- and Eight-Tab Foldable™ *continued*
by Dinah Zike

Vocabulary and Phonics/Spelling Applications
Use the Eight-Tab Foldable to study and review spelling or vocabulary words. For instance, have students do a cumulative study of one of the following:

- phonic elements such as blends and digraphs
- suffixes and prefixes

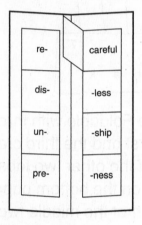

Comprehension Application
The Eight-Tab Foldable is an ideal tool for comparing two texts. Have students use the tabs to compare and contrast four elements: characters, setting, problem, solution. The Foldable is also helpful for summarizing nonfiction.

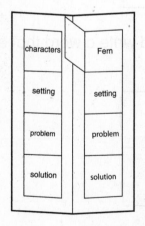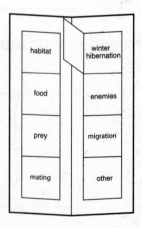

Foldables

Four- and Eight-Tab Foldable™ Directions

by Dinah Zike

Materials:

- one 8½″ × 11″ sheet of paper
- scissors

add these for the Eight-Tab Foldable:

- another 8½″ × 11″ sheet of paper
- one large sheet of construction paper
- glue

Directions:

1. Fold a sheet of paper into a hot dog.

2. With the paper horizontal and the fold of the hot dog at the top, fold the hot dog into four vertical sections.

3. Open these folds. Place one hand between the folded hot dog and cut up the three fold lines so there are four tabs.

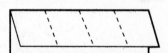

4. To make the Eight-Tab Foldable, follow steps 1-3 with a second sheet of paper. Then fold the construction paper like a hot dog. Open the construction paper. Glue the tabbed hot dogs to the inside so they open like the pages of a book.

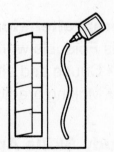

Use this Foldable to _____

_____

Foldables

Using the Matchbook Foldable™ and Portfolio
by Dinah Zike

Vocabulary Application
With students, create Foldables for weekly vocabulary. Write the vocabulary word on the front. Have students write a sentence for the inside.

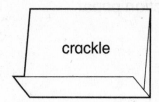

Phonics/Spelling Application
Use the Foldable for review of phonics and/or spelling words.

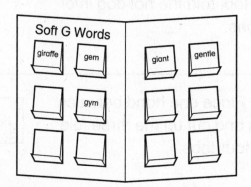

Comprehension Application
This Foldable works for reinforcing skills such as:
- Cause and effect
- Making predictions

Study Skills Application
If students are studying a list such as state capitals or even multiplication tables, the portfolio is a great small group or whole class review tool.

Matchbook Foldable™ and Portfolio Directions
by Dinah Zike

Materials:
- several sheets of 8½″ × 11″ paper
- poster board
- scissors
- glue

Directions:

1. Fold each sheet like a hamburger, but fold it so that one side is one inch longer than the other side.

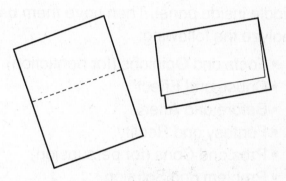

2. Fold the one-inch tab over the short side to form an envelope-like fold.

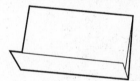

3. Fold each hamburger in half. Cut along the fold line.

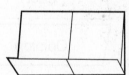

4. Fold the poster board like a hamburger.

5. Use the small hamburgers to record information. Glue them onto the inside of the poster board.

Foldables

Using the Shutter Foldable™
by Dinah Zike

Comprehension Application
There are many ways to use the Shutter Foldable to review and study comprehension skills. Larger paper can be used so that a small group or a class can create one of these for literacy study. Consider having students retell or summarize the story on the middle inside panel. Then have them use the outer panels to analyze the following:

- Facts and Opinions (for nonfiction)
- Cause and Effect
- Before and After
- Fantasy and Reality
- Pros and Cons (for persuasion)
- Problem and Solution
- Compare and Contrast

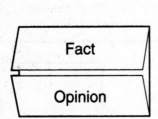

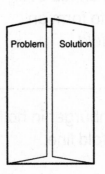

Storage Notes Large Shutter Foldables can be stored in an empty (and clean!) pizza box.

Shutter Foldable™ Directions

by Dinah Zike

Materials:

- 8½″ × 11″ paper

Directions:

1. Begin as if you are going to make a hamburger fold, but instead of folding the paper, pinch it to show the midpoint.

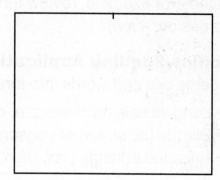

2. Open the sheet. Fold both of the outside edges in to touch the middle mark.

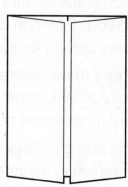

Use this Foldable to _____

_____

_____

_____

_____

© Macmillan/McGraw-Hill

Using the Pyramid Foldable™
by Dinah Zike

Use this Foldable with data occurring in threes.

Vocabulary Application
The Pyramid Foldable can be used to sort and review concepts studied. For example, review three different inflectional endings (*-tion, -sion, -cion*).

Phonics/Spelling Application
Students can sort words into three categories. Some examples:

- Long vowels (such as *o_e, oa, o*)
- Blends (*sl, st, sw*) or consonant digraphs
- Inflected endings (*-ial, -tion, -ious*)

Comprehension Application
Not only can students use the pyramid to record information about what they read, they can do it in a few different ways. With one pyramid they can do things such as the following:

- Compare three different story characters
- Create a K-W-L chart
- Record information about story beginning, middle, and end

Students can glue together three pyramids to create small dioramas depicting scenes (from fiction) and concepts (from nonfiction).

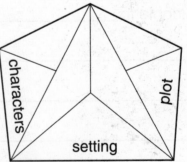

Storage Notes

Several pyramids can be strung together and hung from the ceiling for a vertical display.

Pyramid Foldable™ Directions

by Dinah Zike

Materials:

- one 8½" × 11" sheet of paper
- scissors
- glue

Directions:

1. Fold the sheet into a taco. Cut off the excess rectangular tab formed by the fold.

2. Open the folded taco and refold it like a taco the opposite way to create an X-fold.

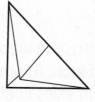

3. Cut one of the valleys to the center of the X, or the midpoint, and stop. This forms two triangular flaps.

4. Glue one of the flaps under the other, forming a pyramid.

Use this Foldable to _____

_____

_____

_____

_____

_____

Using the Two- or Three-Pocket Foldable™
by Dinah Zike

Vocabulary and Phonics/Spelling Applications

Have students use this foldable as a study aid. As they learn words, students may sort and store copies of Spelling Word Cards or Vocabulary Word Cards (see pages 66–95 and 96–125 in this book) in the pockets of this foldable. Have students label the pockets as shown below. As they study the words, have them move the cards to the appropriate pockets.

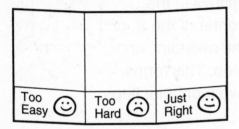 

Comprehension Application

When students are comparing and contrasting ideas in a selection, they can use this foldable to record and store information for retelling or summarizing. This works with skills such as:

- Fact and opinion
- Make and confirm predictions
- Cause and Effect
- K-W-L

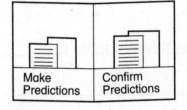

Tip! *Send this foldable home with students so they can review and sort words with family members.*

Storage Notes Heavy stock paper will improve durability. Post the foldable on a bulletin board for use during workstation time.

Foldables

Two- or Three-Pocket Foldable™ Directions

by Dinah Zike

Materials:
- one 11" × 17" sheet of paper
- glue

Directions:

1. Begin as if you are going to make a hot dog, but fold over only about three inches.

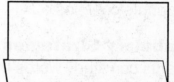

2. Fold the right side toward the center, then fold the left side over the right side to make three sections. (Or, fold in half to make two pockets.)

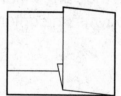

3. Glue the right and left edges of the original fold so that three pockets are created.

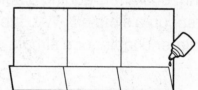

Use this Foldable to _____

_____

_____

_____

_____

Foldables

Using Folded Tables and Charts
by Dinah Zike

Depending upon the amount of data, the table or chart can be adapted and reformatted.

Vocabulary and Phonics/Spelling Applications
Have students use this foldable as a study aid. Have them sort the words into categories and write them in the appropriate columns.

Vocabulary Strategies Application
Students can study words that have:
- prefixes and suffixes
- more than one meaning
- synonyms and antonyms

Multiple Meaning Words		
Word	Definition	Definition

B	M	E

Comprehension Application
Tables such as these can be helpful before, during, and after reading a selection. Students can set up a simple K-W-L table, a beginning-middle-end table, or a simple sequence table.

Storage Notes Set up Vocabulary or Spelling Word binders in workstations so that students have easy access to them.

Foldables

Folded Tables and Charts Directions

by Dinah Zike

Materials:

- one 11" × 17" sheet of paper

Directions:

1. Fold the number of vertical columns needed to make the table (or chart).

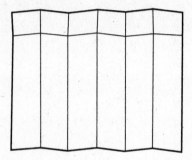

2. Fold the horizontal rows needed to make the table. (If you use loose-leaf paper, you may not need to do this step.)

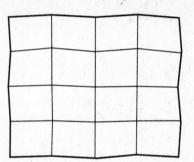

Use this Foldable to _____

_____

_____

_____

_____

_____

_____

_____

Foldables

Foldables™
Correlated to Reading Skills

Foldable	Phonics/Spelling	Vocabulary	Vocabulary Strategies	Comprehension	Study Skills	Grammar
Accordion Book		X	X	X		X
Standing Cube		X		X		X
Large Word Study Book	X	X				
Layered Book	X	X		X	X	X
Four-Door				X		X
Two- and Three-Tab	X			X		
Four- and Eight-Tab	X	X		X		
Matchbook and Portfolio	X	X		X	X	
Shutter				X		
Pyramid	X	X		X		
Two- or Three-Pocket	X	X		X		
Folded Tables and Charts	X	X	X	X		

Learn More About Foldables™

Dinah Zike is the author of more than 150 educational books and materials. For a catalog of Dinah's current publications, as well as information on her keynotes and teacher workshops, call 1-800-99DINAH (1-800-993-4624), or visit her Web site at www.dinah.com.

Look for *Dinah Zike's Big Book of Phonics, Vocabulary, and Spelling* with 260 full-color pages of Foldable activities and word lists for the K–6 classroom.

Look for other practical and inexpensive storage, display, and organization ideas in *Dinah Zike's Classroom Organization: It Can Be Done.* This newly revised and updated publication is perfect for the K–6 classroom teacher who needs to get organized.

Word Study

Use the pages in this section to offer further practice
with phonics, spelling, and word meanings.

rough	stump	jut
tough	nick	shrug
tenth	stuff	laugh
guess	sense	damp
cot	fling	gush
dove	lead	notch
scan	batch	past
dock	plum	cinch
blond		

Spelling Word Cards

folks	aim	prey
yolk	greed	greet
grind	growth	heap
coach	oak	paid
paste	plead	shave
theme	bride	tow
spice	type	tenth
damp	stuff	lifetime
decay		

© Macmillan/McGraw-Hill

amuse	bamboo	brood
crooks	tuna	doom
few	view	hoof
hooks	hue	bruise
booth	lose	duty
handbook	prove	mute
plume	union	coach
theme	bride	strewn
accuse		

Spelling Word Cards

force	scorn	sword
swore	source	aboard
course	coarse	chart
barge	harsh	marsh
starch	heart	scarce
squares	swear	flare
fare	thorn	brood
prove	hoof	uproar
gorge		

squirm	dreary	nerve
squirt	verse	surf
lurk	swerve	stern
spurts	lurch	blurt
thirst	spur	engineer
jeer	sneer	clear
year	yearns	aboard
barge	scarce	smear
rehearse		

Spelling Word Cards

afternoon	background	cornfield
cornmeal	earthworm	flagpole
footstep	mountaintop	overcome
pillowcase	rooftop	cardboard
ice-skating	ninety-one	vice president
all right	field trip	armchair
cheerleader	eggshell	blurt
jeer	thirst	first-class
briefcase		

abilities	countries	batches
difficulties	eddies	fangs
identities	lashes	liberties
notches	possibilities	rattlers
reptiles	rodeos	surroundings
taxes	losses	potatoes
zeroes	beliefs	flagpole
vice president	ninety-one	mangoes
sinews		

amusing	applied	complicated
deserved	dripping	easing
envied	fascinated	forbidding
gnarled	injured	jogging
qualified	raking	regretted
relied	renewing	skimmed
threatening	referred	difficulties
notches	rodeos	adoring
diaries		

bawl	brought	cautious
counter	coil	foul
foundation	fountain	joint
mouthful	dawdle	sprawls
sprouts	turmoil	stout
hoist	clause	turquoise
douse	scrawny	relied
forbidding	easing	buoyant
renown		

Spelling Word Cards

absent	valley	pigment
blizzard	empire	mutter
goggles	fifteen	gallop
dentist	jogger	kennel
summon	champion	mustang
flatter	fragment	hollow
vulture	culture	mouthful
sprawls	sprouts	clammy
hammock		

tyrant	profile	smoky
minus	local	equal
linen	legal	loser
decent	humor	closet
comet	punish	vacant
recent	student	shiver
cavern	panic	valley
fifteen	culture	fatigue
fugitive		

ideas	poet	riot
video	piano	diary
radio	fluid	genuine
rodeo	meteor	cruel
casual	meander	diameter
fuel	patriot	ruin
diet	trial	recent
closet	minus	situation
variety		

orphan	complain	hilltop
concrete	instant	reckless
handsome	fairground	grassland
landlord	pilgrim	district
address	improve	although
partner	footprint	dolphin
cockpit	fiddler	ideas
piano	fuel	mischief
laughter		

python	scorching	season
dozen	motion	phony
active	canvas	expert
embrace	coastal	reserve
govern	flurry	copper
appoint	beside	cocoon
restore	observe	partner
footprint	dolphin	superb
bleachers		

director	shatter	soldier
governor	error	commander
peddler	professor	pillar
splendor	scissors	vapor
scholar	sugar	equator
labor	founder	crater
saucer	gentler	appoint
season	canvas	refrigerator
remainder		

Spelling Word Cards

angle	heron	lengthen
marvel	woolen	listen
bushel	signal	nozzle
practical	barrel	captain
frighten	slogan	mountain
pretzel	fable	global
sandal	chuckle	scissors
pillar	govenor	dungeon
salmon		

© Macmillan/McGraw-Hill

allow	arousing	boundary
bestow	grownup	coward
doubting	rowdy	encounter
power	shower	trousers
grouchy	applause	lawyer
August	laundry	caution
flawless	faucet	angle
mountain	sandal	southern
roughness		

Spelling Word Cards

excuse	contest	content
refuse	protest	conduct
subject	extract	permits
insert	desert	rebel
combat	conflict	research
compact	contract	entrance
present	minute	doubting
allow	caution	effect
affect		

future	creature	searcher
feature	fracture	gesture
legislature	measure	mixture
moisture	nature	pasture
pleasure	azure	stretcher
treasure	rancher	butcher
lecture	pressure	contest
desert	entrance	miniature
disclosure		

Spelling Word Cards

ambulance	appearance	assistance
attendance	brilliance	dependence
substance	disturbance	balance
hesitance	ignorance	importance
performance	persistence	radiance
resistance	reluctance	absence
residence	distance	creature
measure	rancher	vigilance
inference		

agent	baggage	budge
challenge	damage	plunge
jigsaw	jolt	journal
judgment	jumble	knowledge
lodge	luggage	margin
legend	ranger	ridge
surge	dodge	assistance
importance	absence	oxygen
surgeon		

suite	sweet	pier
peer	currant	current
manner	manor	pole
stationary	stationery	waist
waste	peal	peel
presents	presence	council
counsel	kernel	journal
budge	ranger	colonel
poll		

disapprove	discomfort	dishonest
dismount	disobey	mistaken
mistrust	misunderstand	incorrect
preview	preheats	inexpensive
injustice	indefinite	disable
discolor	disconnect	misjudge
prejudge	prewash	presence
stationary	current	prehistoric
misbehave		

bottomless	ceaseless	darkness
effortless	emptiness	fearless
fierceness	fondness	foolishness
forgiveness	fullness	hopeless
gladness	meaningless	harmless
motionless	needless	stillness
sadness	weakness	dishonest
mistaken	preheats	weightlessness
thoughtlessness		

concentrate	concentration	confuse
confusion	correct	correction
decorate	decoration	elect
election	estimate	estimation
exhaust	exhaustion	impress
impression	locate	location
discuss	discussion	hopeless
fearless	forgiveness	conclude
conclusion		

Spelling Word Cards

astronaut	autograph	automatic
automobile	mythical	telegraph
telephone	telescope	television
telegram	homophone	phonics
disaster	astronomer	photograph
photography	myth	mechanic
mechanical	telephoto	correction
discussion	decoration	videophone
photogenic		

suspect	distract	export
inspect	spectator	spectacle
subtraction	tractor	import
transport	transportation	attraction
inspector	missile	mission
committee	intermission	portable
respect	dismiss	telescope
astronaut	photograph	spectacular
protractor		

cereal	terrace	gracious
echo	gigantic	ocean
atlas	clothes	territory
parasol	mortal	fury
furious	January	Olympics
salute	cycle	cyclone
lunar	fortune	suspect
inspect	mission	jovial
venerable		

uniform	bisect	tricycle
triplet	triple	unicorn
unify	unison	universe
unicycle	biweekly	binoculars
triangle	bicycle	trio
century	centipede	centimeter
tripod	university	cereal
terrace	atlas	bilingual
trilogy		

collapsible	breakable	affordable
usable	bearable	favorable
capable	enjoyable	honorable
convertible	invisible	reasonable
respectable	sensible	unbelievable
possible	suitable	laughable
likable	comfortable	uniform
bicycle	triangle	manageable
tangible		

© Macmillan/McGraw-Hill

capable	luminous
categories	slumped
credit	soggy
gigantic	strands

advertisement	impress
commenced	original
elected	sauntered
fireball	wring

buffet	reduce
major	settings
quest	

adjusted	gravity
disasters	maze
environment	mission
function	zone

© Macmillan/McGraw-Hill

canceled	moistened
celebration	theory
cooperation	transformed
fragrance	variety

Vocabulary Word Cards

bulletin board	**mournful**
decency	**shrieks**
delivering	**slurp**
injury	**sympathy**

alert	species
lunging	surroundings
predators	survive
prey	vibrates

artifacts	exhibits
dedicated	site
equality	

blared	hesitation
elegant	irresistible
forbidden	mischievous
gossiped	reluctant

Vocabulary Word Cards

enthusiasm	ravine
flickered	suspended
horizon	swerved
presence	vastness

governor	spunk
instruct	stark
navigation	swagger
patriots	tyrant

attorney	qualify
colonel	representative
legislature	satisfactory
postpone	submit

enlightened	prevailing
humanity	unheeded
inevitable	

Vocabulary Word Cards

brimming	parched
gnarled	progress
gushed	scorching
landscape	scrawny

dangling	robot
defective	rotated
meteor	staggered
reversed	tokens

Vocabulary Word Cards

autograph	fare
blurted	permission
chiseled	scald
clenched	spectacular

arousing	**nestled**
arroyo	**secluded**
behavior	**stunned**
glimpse	**unpleasant**

compelled	presidential
disrespectful	succeed
preoccupied	unenthusiastically

atmosphere	destruction
available	hurricanes
contact	property
damages	surge

appreciation	riverbank
burdens	treasurer
educate	unfortunate
merchandise	wares

abandon	labor
dismantled	treacherous
expedition	triumph
frigid	uninhabited

bedlam	reflected
civilization	shortage
complex	strategy
outcast	traditional

combined	naturalist
diverse	vacant
instill	

Vocabulary Word Cards

corridor	location
creased	reservation
enlisted	sagged
invasion	shield

attraction	**inquire**
discussions	**sprawled**
emerged	**unreasonable**
focused	**ventured**

Vocabulary Word Cards

accompany	descended
bridle	despair
consented	dismiss
delicacies	intentions

bundle	fused
coordination	guaranteed
ease	scenery
frustrated	supervise

Vocabulary Word Cards

elementary	rigid
interact	wheelchair
physical	

anchored	**inflate**
companion	**launched**
dense	**particles**
hydrogen	**scientific**

Vocabulary Word Cards

biology	observer
dormant	research
erupted	scoured
murky	specimens

Learning with Games

Root Word Find

Materials
Puzzle Pieces, three pieces (p. 138)
Vocabulary Word Cards (pp. 96–125)
pencils

Skill: word parts

Prepare: Give players several copies of the three-part puzzle pieces. Have students write each of their vocabulary words onto the puzzle pieces, dividing the words into the appropriate word parts.

Play: Players name the root words, prefixes, suffixes, and/or endings of each word. Call on them or have them quiz each other in small groups.
   If there is time, have players exchange their puzzle pieces with a partner. Have the partner sort the puzzle pieces and put them together to recreate the vocabulary words.

Long Vowel Slip Strips

Materials
Slip Strips or Word Wheel (p. 137, p. 132)
pencils

Skill: build words with long vowel sounds

Prepare: Give each player a copy of the slip strips. Have students write *ay* on the rectangular box to the right of the opening.

Play: Invite players to come up with a variety of words that use the long vowel sound of *ay*. On the slip with four squares, have players write consonants and consonant blends that complete a word. (Players could also use the Word Wheel with *ay* on the outside wheel and consonants and consonant blends on the inside wheel.

The Suffix Trail

Materials
S-shaped board (p. 131)
4-part spinner (p. 129)
Spelling or Vocabulary Word Cards (pp. 66–125)
pencils

Skill: suffixes

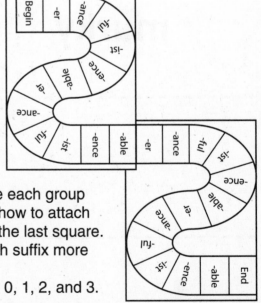

Prepare: This game is for three or four players. Give each group two copies of the S-shaped game board. Show them how to attach the copies. Write *begin* in the first square and *end* in the last square. Then fill the remaining squares with suffixes. Use each suffix more than once.
   Each group also needs a 4-part spinner numbered 0, 1, 2, and 3.

Play: Players spin the spinner then move that number of spaces. Then the player must say a word that has the suffix shown. Players may refer to the Spelling or Vocabulary Word Cards. The game ends when a player reaches the *end* square.

Match!

Materials
> Cards (p. 133)
> pencils

Skill: homophones

Prepare: This game is for two players. Give each pair four copies of the cards. Have partners write homophones on the cards. They may use the following words: *would, wood; right, write; flour, flower; know, no; passed, past; here, hear; seam, seem; weak, week; maid, made; fined, find; scent, cent; patience, patients; see, sea; ate, eight; meat, meet.*

Play: Begin by dealing ten cards to each player. Each player looks for any homophone matches and places them on the table. Then players take turns asking each other if they hold the match to one of their own cards. A player draws from the remaining cards if the opposing player cannot give the requested homonym. The player who ends up with the most matches is the winner.

Four Corners

Materials
> Tic-Tac-Toe grid (p. 134)
> pencils
> game markers

Skill: contractions

Prepare: Give each player a copy of the Tic-Tac-Toe grid. Have the players write a different contraction in each corner. You may want to write the following contractions on the board for reference: *won't, I've, wasn't, it's, doesn't, haven't, isn't, you'll, aren't, you've, let's, we're, that's, don't, couldn't, wouldn't, he's, she's.*

Play: Call out the two words that make the different contractions. Have players place a marker on the correct contraction. For example, if you call out *will + not,* the players place a marker on *won't.* The winner is the first player to place a marker in each of the four corners of the Tic-Tac-Toe grid.

Games

Look It Up!

Materials
- 4-part spinner (p. 129)
- Oval board (p. 130)
- Vocabulary Word Cards (pp. 96–125)
- dictionary
- pencils

Skill: dictionary skills

Prepare: This game is for three or four players. Give each group an oval board, a blank spinner, and a dictionary. On the board, mark one square with a star to indicate the beginning and ending point. Have them fill the other squares with current and review vocabulary words. They may refer to their Vocabulary Words Cards for word suggestions.

Label the spinner 1 *Definition,* 2 *Pronunciation Key,* 3 *Word History,* and 0.

Play: Players spin the spinner and move that number of spaces. (0 = skip turn) The spinner will also tell them what they need to find out about the word they landed on. Players use the dictionary to tell the word's definition, pronunciation key, or history. The winner is the first player to reach the star.

Coin Toss

Materials
- 4 x 4 or 5 x 5 grid (p. 135, p. 136)
- pencil
- penny

Skill: fact and opinion

Prepare: This game is for four players. Give each group a copy of the 4 x 4 grid. Have each player write his or her name in the first square of one row.

Play: The object of the game is to be the first player to color in each square in their row. Each player flips a penny. If the coin lands on "heads," then the player tells a fact about the school. The player also colors in a square. If the coin lands on "tails," then the player gives an opinion about the school. Players cannot color in a square if they get tails.

Use the 5 x 5 grid if there are five players in a group. To make the game more advanced, have players offer facts and opinions about stories or topics to complete the game.

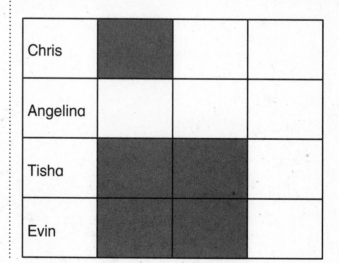

Games

Spinners

1. Cut out and complete a spinner.

2. Mount it on heavy paper.

3. Attach arrow with brad.

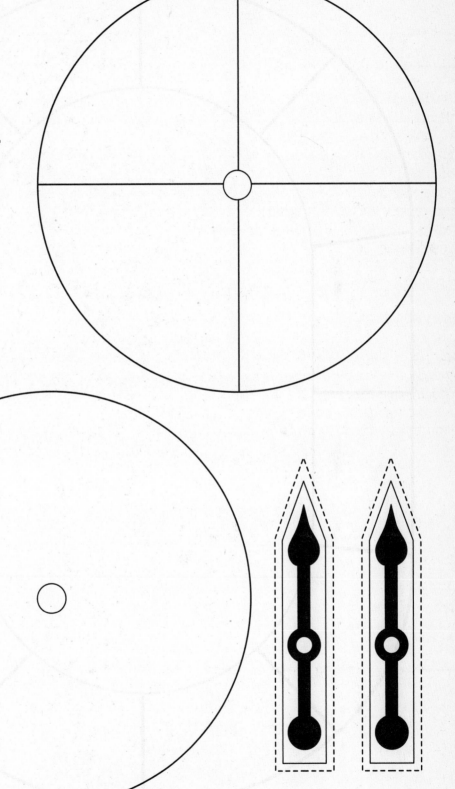

Oval Game Board

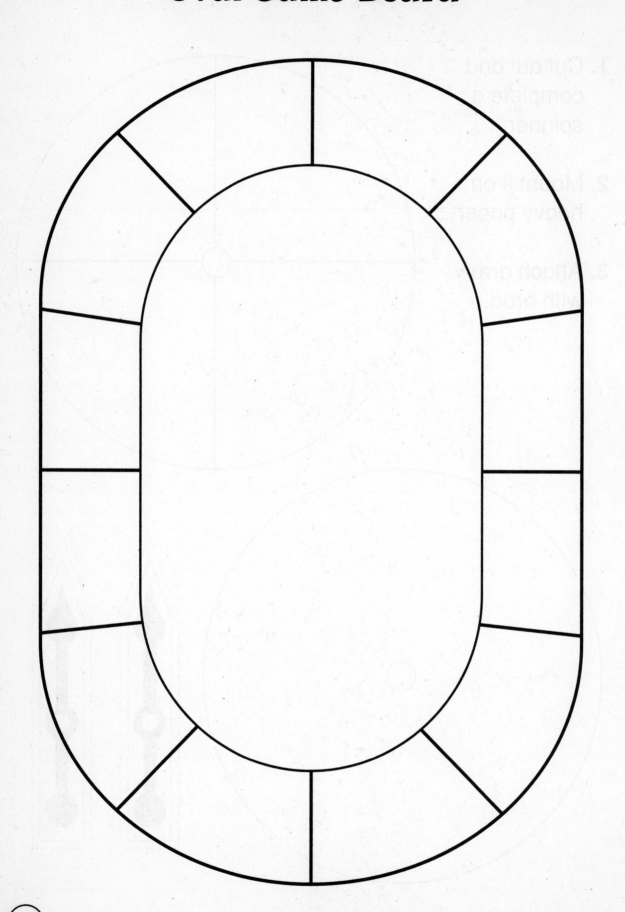

Games

S-shaped Game Board

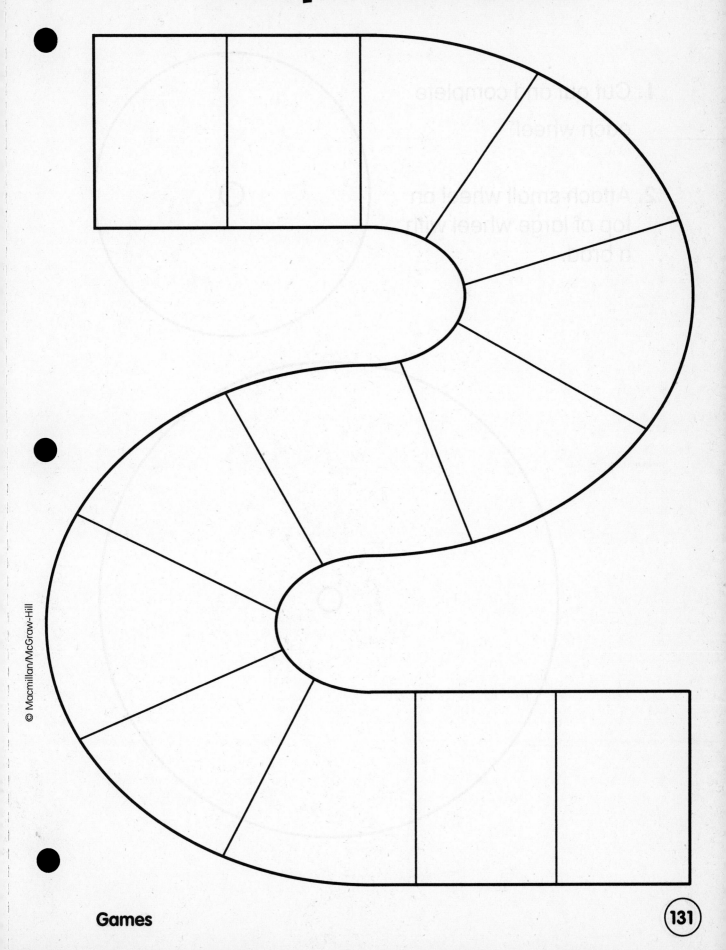

Games

Word Wheel

1. Cut out and complete each wheel.

2. Attach small wheel on top of large wheel with a brad.

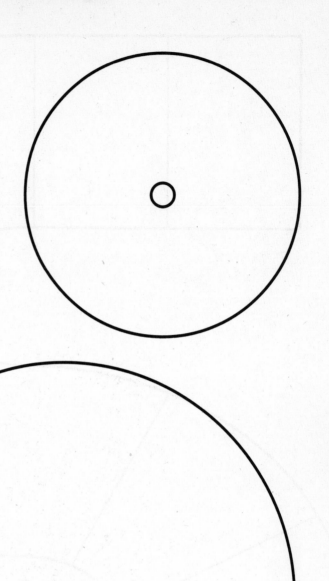

Cards

Games

Tic-Tac-Toe

Games

4x4 Grid

5x5 Grid

Slip Strips

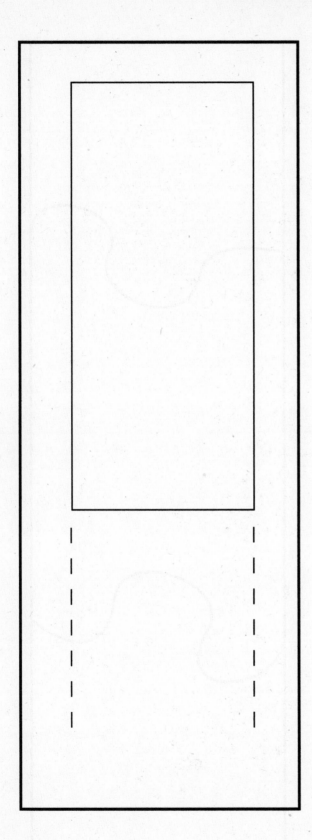

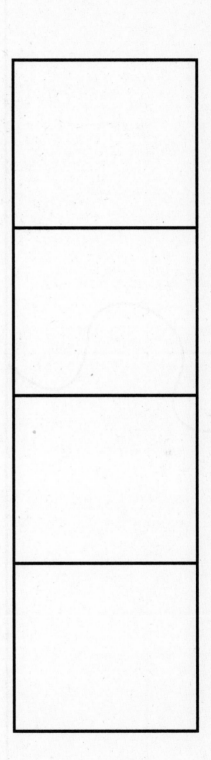

Puzzle Pieces

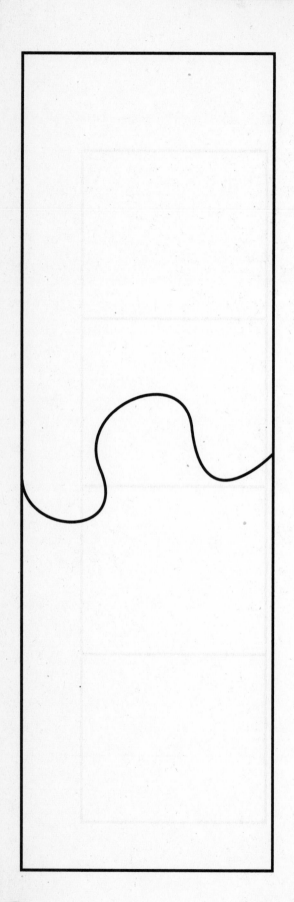

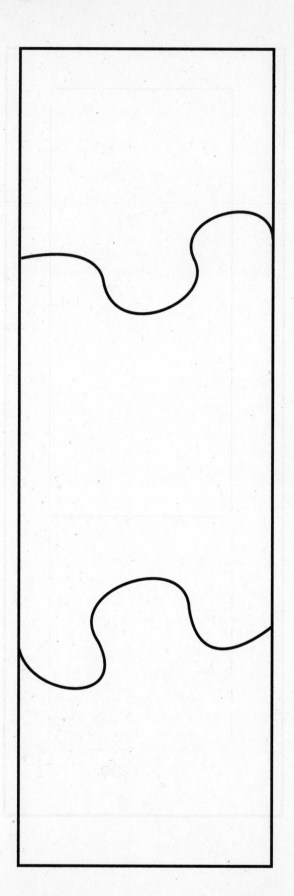

Additional Literacy Support

Use the pages in this section to support reading, writing, handwriting, listening, and speaking activities.

Name _____

Reader Response

Title: _____ Author: _____

Rate this book by coloring in the stars.

Awesome   Good   Okay   Disliked   Disliked a lot

Recommendation: To whom would you recommend this book?

_____

Response: Write one of the following as if it were from the point of view of a particular character.

_____ Poem   _____ One-act play

_____ Song   _____ Journal entry

_____

_____

_____

_____

_____

Reader Response: Fiction

Name _____

Reader Response

Title: _____ Author: _____

Rate this book by coloring in the stars.

Awesome   Good   Okay   Disliked   Disliked a lot

Recommendation: To whom would you recommend this book?

_____

Response: Write a new ending to this story. How will it affect the rest of the story?

_____

_____

_____

_____

_____

_____

_____

Reader Response: Fiction

Name _____

Reader Response

Title: _____ Author: _____

Rate this book by coloring in the stars.

☆   ☆   ☆   ☆   ☆

Awesome   Good   Okay   Disliked   Disliked a lot

Recommendation: To whom would you recommend this book?

_____

Response: What was the most surprising or interesting thing you learned? Choose one of the following to write your response.

_____ Magazine article   _____ Book review

_____ Letter to a friend   _____ Journal entry

_____

_____

_____

_____

Reader Response: Nonfiction

Name _____

Reader Response

Title: _____ Author: _____

Rate this book by coloring in the stars.

Awesome   Good   Okay   Disliked   Disliked a lot

Recommendation: To whom would you recommend this book?

_____

Response: Write an e-mail to the author describing what you have learned from this book.

To: _____ @example.com

Subject: _____

Dear_____:

_____

_____

Sincerely,

_____

Reader Response: Nonfiction

Name _____

Reader Response

Title: _____ Author: _____

Rate this poem by coloring in the stars.

☆ ☆ ☆ ☆ ☆

Awesome   Good   Okay   Disliked   Disliked a lot

Recommendation: To whom would you recommend this poem?

_____

Response: Is this poem like any other poem you have read before? Why?

_____

_____

_____

_____

_____

_____

Name _____

Reader Response

Title: _____ Author: _____

Rate this poem by coloring in the stars.

Awesome   Good   Okay   Disliked   Disliked a lot

Recommendation: To whom would you recommend this poem?

_____

Response: Describe how you feel about this poem. What do you like or dislike about this poem?

_____

_____

_____

_____

_____

_____

My Writer's Checklist
Personal Narrative

✔ **Put a check by the items you completed.**

☐	Do I tell a true story about something that happened to me?
☐	Do I tell how I am feeling?
☐	Do I tell the events of my story in the sequence in which they happened?
☐	Do I use first person pronouns to personalize my story?
☐	Do I use time-order words to help the reader follow the sequence of events?

What did I do well in my writing?

1. _____

2. _____

What will I change when I revise this work?

1. _____

2. _____

Teacher: See also Proofreading Marks, page 152, and Writing Rubrics, pages 153–160.

My Writer's Checklist
Persuasive Writing

✔ **Put a check by the items you completed.**

☐	Do I clearly state my opinion in the opening paragraph?
☐	Do I give explanations, facts, and examples to support my opinion?
☐	Do I present my reasons in a logical order with the strongest reason appearing last?
☐	Do I tell my feelings about the topic?
☐	Do I use opinion words?

What did I do well in my writing?

1. _____

2. _____

What will I change when I revise this work?

1. _____

2. _____

Teacher: See also Proofreading Marks, page 152, and Writing Rubrics, pages 153–160.

Name _____

My Writer's Checklist
Fictional Narrative

✔ **Put a check by the items you completed.**

☐	Do I focus my story on a main character who is faced with a decision?
☐	Does my story have a beginning, a middle, and an end?
☐	Do I set up a problem for the main character and then tell a solution?
☐	Do I include figurative language to help the reader visualize events?
☐	Do my sentences flow together to tell a good story as I read it aloud?

What did I do well in my writing?

1. _____

2. _____

What will I change when I revise this work?

1. _____

2. _____

Teacher: See also Proofreading Marks, page 152, and Writing Rubrics, pages 153–160.

© Macmillan/McGraw-Hill

Name _____

My Writer's Checklist
Research Report

✔ **Put a check by the items you completed.**

☐	Do I provide facts and details to explain my main idea?
☐	Do I have a strong introduction?
☐	Do I close by drawing a conclusion that links to the introduction?
☐	Do I present research from a variety of sources?
☐	Do I connect my points with transition words?

What did I do well in my writing?

1. _____

2. _____

What will I change when I revise this work?

1. _____

2. _____

Teacher: See also Proofreading Marks, page 152, and Writing Rubrics, pages 153–160.

Name _____

My Writer's Checklist
Compare and Contrast

✔ **Put a check by the items you completed.**

☐	Do I tell what is being compared in the first sentence?
☐	Do I order my information either point by point or item by item?
☐	Do I summarize my most important points in the conclusion?
☐	Do I use exact terms to make my description of the topics clear and precise?
☐	Do I vary the types of sentences I use with some long and some short sentences?

What did I do well in my writing?

1. _____

2. _____

What will I change when I revise this work?

1. _____

2. _____

Teacher: See also Proofreading Marks, page 152, and Writing Rubrics, pages 153–160.

My Writer's Checklist

How-to Article

✔ **Put a check by the items you completed.**

☐	Do I explain how to complete a specific task?
☐	Do I provide clear details that the reader can follow?
☐	Are my instructions presented step-by-step in a logical order?
☐	Do I include time-order words or spatial words that make my instructions clear?
☐	Do I vary the types and lengths of sentences?

What did I do well in my writing?

1. _____

2. _____

What will I change when I revise this work?

1. _____

2. _____

Teacher: See also Proofreading Marks, page 152, and Writing Rubrics, pages 153–160.

Proofreading Marks

≡	Make a capital letter.	<u>we</u> went to the park. ≡
/	Make a small letter.	We walked by the /Lake.
⊙	Add a period.	The fish were jumping ⊙
∧	Add a comma.	I saw ants∧frogs, and a bird.
⌄⌄ ⌄⌄	Add quotation marks.	⌄⌄What time is it?⌄⌄asked Mom.
⌄	Add an apostrophe.	Dan⌄s watch was broken.
(sp)	Check spelling.	The sky was (beuatiful.) (sp)
∧	Add.	*we* Then∧ate lunch.
℘	Take out.	The ~~tall~~ trees were very tall.
(tr) ⌐⌐	Switch the order.	Fishermen came often to the lake. (tr)
‿	Close up.	We had a prob‿lem.
#	Add a space.	# Look at the∧sunset.
¶	New paragraph	¶ The town seemed busy and noisy after our day at the park.

Writing Rubric

	4 Excellent	3 Good	2 Fair	1 Unsatisfactory
	• tells an entertaining story about a personal experience and includes thoughts and feelings	• tells about a personal experience and includes some thoughts and feelings	• tells about a personal experience but focus often strays from the experience	• does not share a personal experience and is not focused or entertaining
	• presents details in an easy-to-follow sequence	• presents details in the correct order	• includes events that are told out of order	• tells events out of order and is confusing
	• always uses the first person and clearly expresses feelings	• mostly uses the first person and expresses feelings	• does not always use the first person and does not express enough feelings	• does not use first person and does not express feelings
	• always uses the first person and uses many time-order words	• mostly uses the first person and uses some time-order words	• does not use the first person enough and lacks time-order words	• does not use the first person or time-order words
	• varies types and lengths of sentences	• includes both simple and compound sentences	• uses only simple sentences	• sentences are choppy or run together
	• is free or almost free of errors	• has minor errors that do not confuse the reader	• makes frequent errors that confuse the reader	• makes serious and repeated errors
	• is easy to read and free of word processing or handwriting distractions	• is mostly easy to read and mostly free of word processing or handwriting distractions	• is readable, but handwriting or word processing errors are distracting	• is difficult to read because of word processing or handwriting errors

Writing Rubric

4 Excellent	3 Good	2 Fair	1 Unsatisfactory
• presents a focused, clear opinion with supporting details	• presents a clear opinion with supporting details	• attempts to present an opinion but does not include enough supporting details	• does not present an opinion
• presents reasons for an opinion in a logical order, with strongest reason last	• presents reasons for an opinion in a logical order	• presents reasons for the opinion, but not in the most logical order	• misses reasons or presents reasons in a confusing order
• engages readers with a strong opinion and a personal tone	• makes a strong attempt at using a personal tone to present personal opinions	• does not communicate a personal opinion and uses little personal tone	• lacks any personal tone that engages readers
• uses many well-chosen opinion words	• uses several well-chosen opinion words	• uses only one or two opinion words that are not well-chosen	• does not use opinion words
• uses a variety of sentence types that begin in different ways	• uses a variety of sentence types	• is choppy and distracting	• uses sentence fragments and run-on sentences
• is free or almost free of errors	• has minor errors that do not confuse the reader	• makes frequent errors that confuse the reader	• makes serious and repeated errors
• is easy to read and free of word processing or handwriting distractions	• is mostly easy to read and mostly free of word processing or handwriting distractions	• is readable, but handwriting or word processing errors are distracting	• is difficult to read because of word processing or handwriting errors

Writing Rubric

4 Excellent	3 Good	2 Fair	1 Unsatisfactory
• creates an imaginative, entertaining story	• creates an imaginative, interesting story	• creates a fairly imaginative story, but story lacks details about characters and plot	• creates a story lacking in imagination
• has a carefully planned narrative with an engaging beginning, middle, and end	• has a well-planned plot with a clear beginning, middle, and end	• has a confusing narrative	• presents story details in a confusing, illogical manner
• uses a clear and believable voice and unique narrative style	• uses an original voice that is consistent with the plot and characters	• attempts a narrative voice but does not engage or entertain the reader	• does not use a distinct narrative voice
• uses rich, precise language, including figurative language	• uses clear, concise language with both new and everyday words	• uses ordinary language and repeats words or phrases	• uses words that are either incorrect or do not fit with the story
• includes a variety of sentences that have rhythm and flow	• includes both simple and compound sentences	• includes sentences of little variety in structure	• uses sentences that are too long or too short and that do not express thoughts clearly
• is free or almost free of errors	• has minor errors that do not confuse the reader	• makes frequent errors that confuse the reader	• makes serious and repeated errors
• is easy to read and free of word processing or handwriting distractions	• is mostly easy to read and mostly free of word processing or handwriting distractions	• is readable, but handwriting or word processing errors are distracting	• is difficult to read because of word processing or handwriting errors

Writing Rubric

	4 Excellent	3 Good	2 Fair	1 Unsatisfactory
	• uses reliable sources and has interesting, unusual facts	• uses reliable sources and has a main idea and supporting details	• presents a report with some facts based on limited research	• presents a report that is not researched with either no or inaccurate facts
	• is well structured, with a strong introduction and a final conclusion	• has a logical flow of facts and details	• has sections that are hard to follow	• is structured poorly and is impossible to follow
	• shows awareness of readers and a sense of purpose throughout	• shows a good awareness of readers and a sense of purpose	• does not show awareness of readers, and shows little understanding of topic	• does not address readers and shows little or no understanding of topic
	• uses transition words and a vivid vocabulary	• uses words appropriate to topic and includes transition words to connect ideas	• chooses poor words for topic and includes few transition words	• uses only basic vocabulary and does not use transition words
	• includes sentences that flow and hold the reader's interest	• uses a variety of simple and complex sentences	• uses choppy sentences and awkward phrasing	• includes incomplete and run-on sentences
	• is free or almost free of errors	• has minor errors that do not confuse the reader	• makes frequent errors that confuse the reader	• makes serious and repeated errors
	• is easy to read and free of word processing or handwriting distractions	• is mostly easy to read and mostly free of word processing or handwriting distractions	• is readable, but handwriting or word processing errors are distracting	• is difficult to read because of word processing or handwriting errors

Writing Rubric

	4 Excellent	3 Good	2 Fair	1 Unsatisfactory
	• compares and contrasts two items or topics, with supporting details	• compares and contrasts two items or topics	• writes an unclear comparison with few details	• does not write a comparison of two items or topics
	• organizes the comparison in a way that guides readers, and includes a conclusion	• organizes the comparison well and draws a conclusion	• does not organize the comparison clearly and does not include a conclusion	• has no organization or flow
	• uses a clear voice that shows detailed knowledge	• attempts to connect with readers in a voice that shows knowledge	• does not connect well with reader and shows incomplete knowledge	• does not connect with readers and shows little or no knowledge of items or topics
	• uses precise compare and contrast words	• uses compare and contrast words correctly	• uses few compare or contrast words	• uses only general words or uses words incorrectly
	• writes sentences in which ideas flow smoothly	• writes simple sentences that can be easily read aloud	• writes choppy sentences that are hard to follow	• includes incomplete and/ or run-on sentences
	• is free or almost free of errors	• has minor errors that do not confuse the reader	• makes frequent errors that confuse the reader	• makes serious and repeated errors
	• is easy to read and free of word processing or handwriting distractions	• is mostly easy to read and mostly free of word processing or handwriting distractions	• is readable, but handwriting or word processing errors are distracting	• is difficult to read because of word processing or handwriting errors

Writing Rubric

4 Excellent	3 Good	2 Fair	1 Unsatisfactory
• creates a focused explanation with clear details	• creates a solid explanation with clear details	• attempts an explanation, but some details may be unclear	• creates an incomplete explanation
• explains the task in an engaging way, with steps presented in a logical order	• introduces the topic and presents steps in a logical order	• presents some steps out of order	• does not include a clear beginning and presents steps illogically
• uses a personal style and shows an original knowledge of the task	• uses a personal tone and shows knowledge of the task	• does not connect to the readers with enthusiasm	• does not use a personal voice and shows little knowledge of the topic
• uses time-order words and precise verbs	• includes some time-order words and some precise verbs	• includes few time-order words and uses unclear verbs	• uses words that do not explain the task, with no time-order words
• uses a variety of simple and complex sentences that flow	• includes a variety of easy-to-follow sentences	• includes readable sentences, but sentences lack variety	• includes incomplete and confusing sentences
• is free or almost free of errors	• has minor errors that do not confuse the reader	• makes frequent errors that confuse the reader	• makes serious and repeated errors
• is easy to read and free of word processing or handwriting distractions	• is mostly easy to read and mostly free of word processing or handwriting distractions	• is readable, but handwriting or word processing errors are distracting	• is difficult to read because of word processing or handwriting errors

Writing Rubric

	④ Excellent	③ Good	② Fair	① Unsatisfactory
	• Ideas and Content	• Ideas and Content	• Ideas and Content	• Ideas and Content
	• Organization	• Organization	• Organization	• Organization
	• Voice	• Voice	• Voice	• Voice
	• Word Choice	• Word Choice	• Word Choice	• Word Choice
	• Sentence Fluency	• Sentence Fluency	• Sentence Fluency	• Sentence Fluency
	• Conventions	• Conventions	• Conventions	• Conventions
	• Presentation	• Presentation	• Presentation	• Presentation

Writing Rubric

4 Excellent	3 Good	2 Fair	1 Unsatisfactory

Writing to a Picture Prompt

Students are sometimes asked to write about a picture instead of just responding to a writing prompt. The student will either tell about what they see in the picture, or write about something related to the picture. The form of the writing is usually a story or an essay.

Use the picture prompts as additional writing practice or to help students prepare for writing tasks on standardized tests.

Instruct students to do the following:

Before Writing

1. Look closely at the picture. Think about what is happening in the picture.
2. Ask yourself questions about the picture:
   - Where and when are the events shown in the picture taking place?
   - Who or what is in the picture? What are they doing?
   - Can you tell what is happening? What event may have happened prior to this one? What do you think might happen next?
3. You can use a graphic organizer to organize your ideas before you begin to write. You can also make an outline, create an idea web, or do other prewriting work.

During Writing

Use a graphic organizer, or other prewriting work, to write about what is happening in the picture.

After Writing

1. Use the Writer's Checklists, pages 146–151, to help you check your writing.
2. Proofread your writing using Proofreading Marks, page 152.

Name _____

Write to a picture prompt. Why are trees important? Look at the photograph below. Write a story about what might happen if trees disappeared from your community.

 Writing Tips

- Use a graphic organizer to organize your thoughts.
- Write your story on lined paper.
- Proofread your story.

Name _____

Write to a picture prompt. The picture below shows the Tomb of the Unknowns, a memorial to American soldiers of four wars. Write a story about visiting a war memorial.

 Writing Tips

- Use a graphic organizer to organize your thoughts.
- Write your story on lined paper.
- Proofread your story.

Name _____

Write to a picture prompt. Look at the picture below. Write a story about protecting the environment.

WE
RECYCLE

 Writing Tips

• Use a graphic organizer to organize your thoughts.
• Write your story on lined paper.
• Proofread your story.

Write to a picture prompt. Look at the picture below. Write a story about how one vote can make a difference.

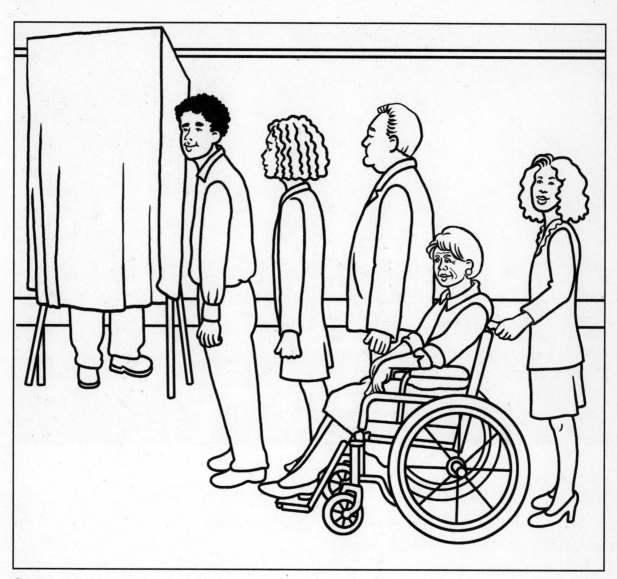

 Writing Tips

- Use a graphic organizer to organize your thoughts.
- Write your story on lined paper.
- Proofread your story.

Write to a picture prompt. Suppose you are hiking with the boy in the photograph below. Write a story about what you see and do on the hike.

 ## Writing Tips

- Use a graphic organizer to organize your thoughts.
- Write your story on lined paper.
- Proofread your story.

Write to a picture prompt. Look at the photograph below. Write a story about inventing a new way of helping somebody else.

 Writing Tips

- Use a graphic organizer to organize your thoughts.
- Write your story on lined paper.
- Proofread your story.

Handwriting

A Communication Tool
Although computers are available, many tasks require handwriting. Keeping journals, completing forms, taking notes, making shopping or organizational lists, and reading handwriting are practical uses of this skill.

Writing Readiness
Before students begin to write, they need to develop certain fine motor skills. These are examples of warm-up activities:

- Play "Simon Says" using fingers only.
- Sing finger plays such as "Where Is Thumbkin?" and "The Eensie Weensie Spider," or songs that use Signed English or American Sign Language.
- Use mazes that require students to move their writing instruments from left to right.

Determining Handedness
Keys to determining handedness in a student:

- With which hand does the student eat? This hand is likely to become the dominant hand.
- Does the student start coloring with one hand and then switch to the other? This may be due to fatigue or lack of hand preference.
- Does the student cross midline to pick things up? Place items directly in front of the student to see if one hand is preferred.
- Does the student do better with one hand or the other?

The Mechanics of Writing
Desk and Chair
- Chair height should allow feet to rest flat on the floor.
- Desk height should be two inches above the level of the elbows when the student is sitting.

- There should be an inch between the student and the desk.
- The student should sit erect with elbows resting on the desk.
- Models of letters should be on the desk or at eye level.

Paper Position
- Right-handed students should turn the paper so that the lower left-hand of the paper points to the abdomen.
- Left-handed students should turn the paper so that the lower right-hand of the paper points to the abdomen.
- The nondominant hand should anchor the paper near the top so that the paper doesn't slide.
- The student should move the paper up as he or she nears the bottom of the paper. Many students do not think of this.

The Writing Instrument Grasp
The writing instrument must be held in a way that allows for fluid dynamic movement.

Functional Grasp Patterns
- <u>Tripod Grasp</u> With open web space, the writing instrument is held with the tip of the thumb and the index finger and rests against the side of the third finger. The thumb and index finger form a circle.

- **Quadrupod Grasp** With open web space, the writing instrument is held with the tip of the thumb and index finger and rests against the fourth finger. The thumb and index finger form a circle.

Incorrect Grasp Patterns

- **Fisted Grasp** The writing instrument is held in a fisted hand.

- **Pronated Grasp** The writing instrument is held diagonally within the hand with the tips of the thumb and index finger on the writing instrument but with no support from other fingers.

- **Five-Finger Grasp** The writing instrument is held with the tips of all five fingers.

- **Flexed or Hooked Wrist** A flexed or bent wrist is typical with left-handed writers and is also present in some right-handed writers.

Correcting Grasp Patterns

- Have students play counting games with an eye dropper and water.
- Have students pick up small objects with a tweezer.
- Have students pick up small coins using just the thumb and index finger.
- To correct wrist position, have students check their posture and paper placement.

Evaluation Checklist

Functional handwriting is made up of two elements, legibility and functional speed.

Legibility in Writing

Formation and Strokes

- ☑ Do circular shapes close?
- ☑ Are downstrokes parallel?
- ☑ Do circular shapes and downstrokes touch?
- ☑ Are the heights of capital letters equal?
- ☑ Are the heights of lowercase letters equal?
- ☑ Are the lengths of the extenders and descenders the same for all letters?
- ☑ Do cursive letters that finish at the top join the next letter? (*b, o, v, w*)
- ☑ Do cursive letters that finish at the bottom join the next letter? (*a, c, d, e, h, i, k, l, m, n, r, s, t, u, x*)
- ☑ Do cursive letters with descenders join the next letter? (*f, g, j, p, q, y, z*)

- ☑ Is the slant of all letters consistent?
- ☑ Do all letters rest on the line?

Directionality

- ☑ Are letters and words formed from left to right?
- ☑ Are letters and words formed from top to bottom?

Spacing

- ☑ Are the spaces between letters equal?
- ☑ Are the spaces between words equal?
- ☑ Are spaces between sentences equal?
- ☑ Are spaces between paragraphs equal?
- ☑ Are top, bottom, and side margins even?

Speed

The prettiest handwriting is not functional if it takes students too long to complete their work. After introducing students to writing individual letters, add time limits to copying or writing assignments. Check for legibility.

Handwriting Basics

Handwriting Models – Manuscript

A B C D E F G H

I J K L M N O P

Q R S T U V W

X Y Z

a b c d e f g h

i j k l m n o p q

r s t u v w x y z

Handwriting Models – Cursive

A B C D E F G H

I J K L M N O P Q

R S T U V W X Y Z

a b c d e f g h i j

k l m n o p q r s

t u v w x y z

A B C D E F G H I

J K L M N O P Q R

S T U V W X Y Z

a b c d e f g h

i j k l m n o p q

r s t u v w x y z

Handwriting Practice

Good Listening and Speaking Habits

In our classroom we:

- Follow class procedures and rules

- Respect other people's feelings and ideas

- Speak clearly so that others can understand

- Listen to one another thoughtfully

- Take turns speaking

- Do not criticize people because of their ideas

- Ask good questions

- Do our best and encourage others to do their best

- Answer questions thoughtfully

- Work collaboratively in small groups so that everyone can learn

Classroom Behavior Checklist